PREAM GRAPHICS

SWITCH FACE

JONNY ZUCKER AND KEV HOPGOOD

EDGE
FRANKLIN WATTS

LONDON•SYDNEY

SWITCH
FACE

When Luke looks at a photo
and rubs his face, he takes on the
appearance of the person in the photo!

When he rubs his face again
he switches back to his own face.

First published in 2013 by
Franklin Watts
338 Euston Road
London NW1 3BH

Franklin Watts Australia
Level 17/207 Kent Street
Sydney, NSW 2000

Text © Jonny Zucker 2013
Illustrations © Franklin Watts 2013

The rights of Jonny Zucker to be
identified as the author and Kev Hopgood
as the illustrator of this Work have
been asserted in accordance with the
Copyright, Designs and Patents Act, 1988.

A CIP catalogue record for this book
is available from the British Library.

(ebook) ISBN: 978 1 4451 1810 9
(pb) ISBN: 978 1 4451 1804 8
(Library ebook) ISBN: 978 1 4451 2614 2

Series Editors: Adrian Cole and Jackie Hamley
Series Advisors: Diana Bentley and Dee Reid
Series Designer: Peter Scoulding

A paperback original

1 3 5 7 9 10 8 6 4 2

Printed in China

Franklin Watts is a division of
Hachette Children's Books,
an Hachette UK company
www.hachette.co.uk

About

SLIPSTREAM

Slipstream is a series of expertly levelled books designed for pupils who are struggling with reading. Its unique three-strand approach through fiction, graphic fiction and non-fiction gives pupils a rich reading experience that will accelerate their progress and close the reading gap.

At the heart of every Slipstream graphic fiction book is a great story. Easily accessible words and phrases ensure that pupils both decode and comprehend, and the high interest stories really engage older struggling readers.

Whether you're using Slipstream Level 1 for Guided Reading or as an independent read, here are some suggestions:

1. Make each reading session successful. Talk about the text or pictures before the pupil starts reading. Introduce any unfamiliar vocabulary.

2. Encourage the pupil to talk about the book using a range of open questions. For example, what do they think will happen to Luke after he is taken to the police station?

3. Discuss the differences between reading fiction, graphic fiction and non-fiction. What do they prefer?

Slipstream Level 1 photocopiable **WORKBOOK** ISBN: 978 1 4451 1798 0 available – download free sample worksheets from: www.franklinwatts.co.uk

For guidance, SLIPSTREAM Level 1 – Switch Face has been approximately measured to:

National Curriculum Level: 2c
Reading Age: 7.0–7.6
Book Band: Turquoise

ATOS: 1.7*
Guided Reading Level: H
Lexile® Measure (confirmed): 160L

*Please check actual Accelerated Reader™ book level and quiz availability at www.arbookfind.co.uk